Hap is Hot

By Kevin Reese

Illustrated by Chad Thompson

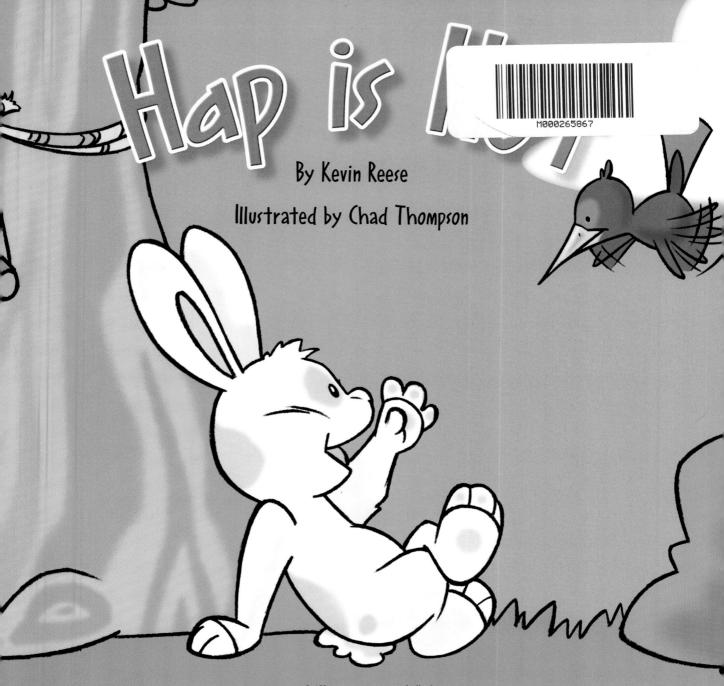

Target Skill Consonant *Hh*/h/

PEARSON

Scott Foresman

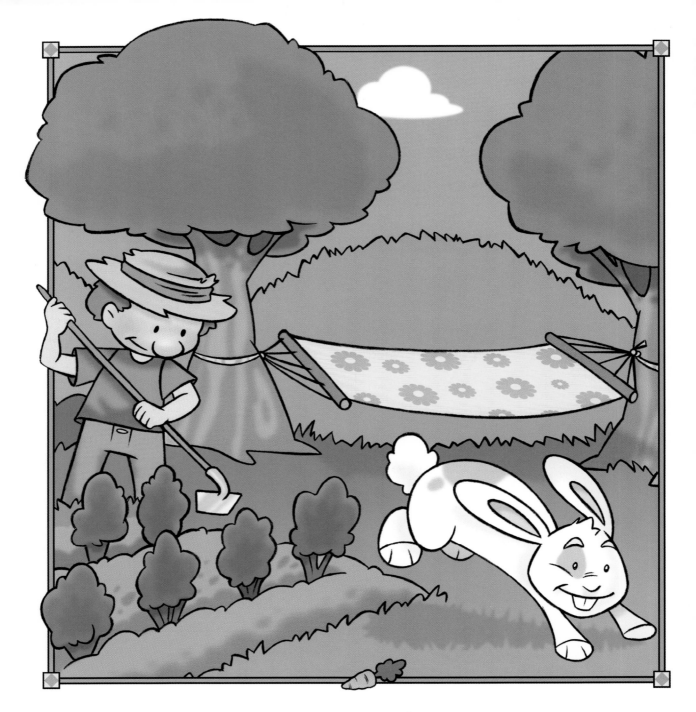

Hap can hop.

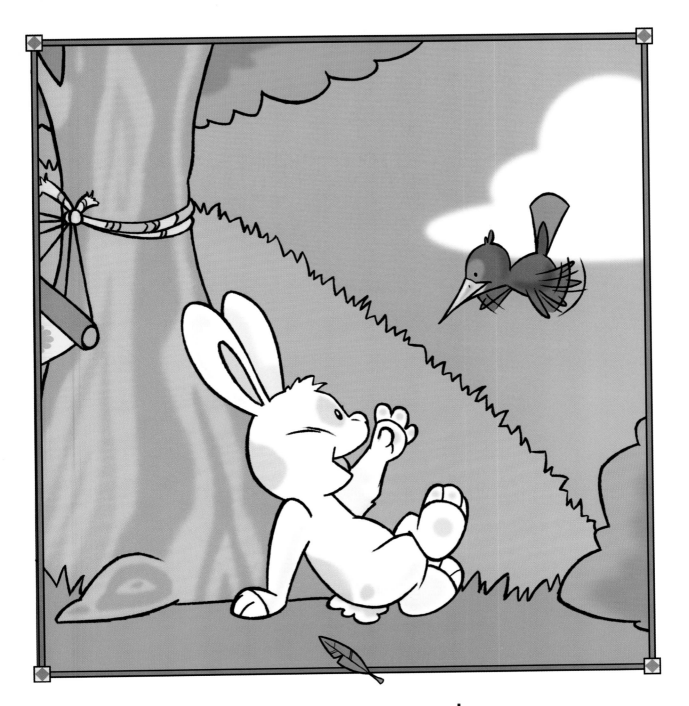

Hap can sit a bit.

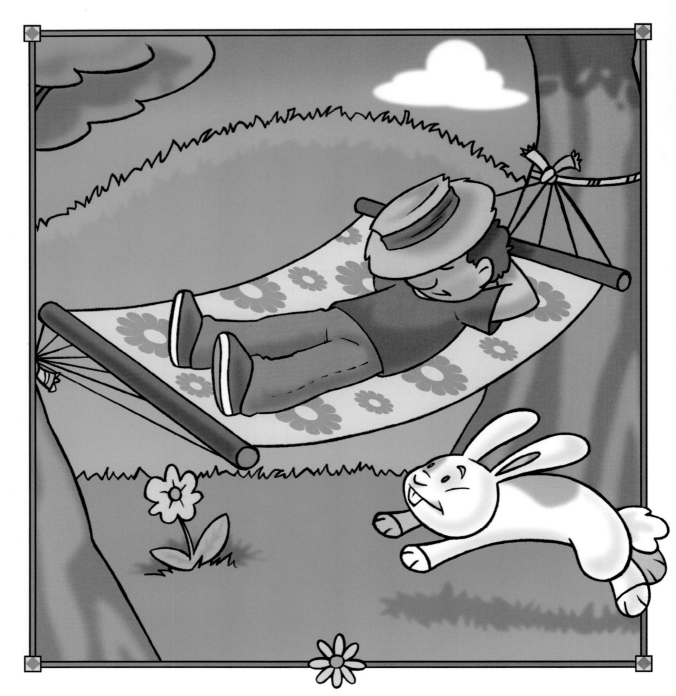

Hap can hop a bit.

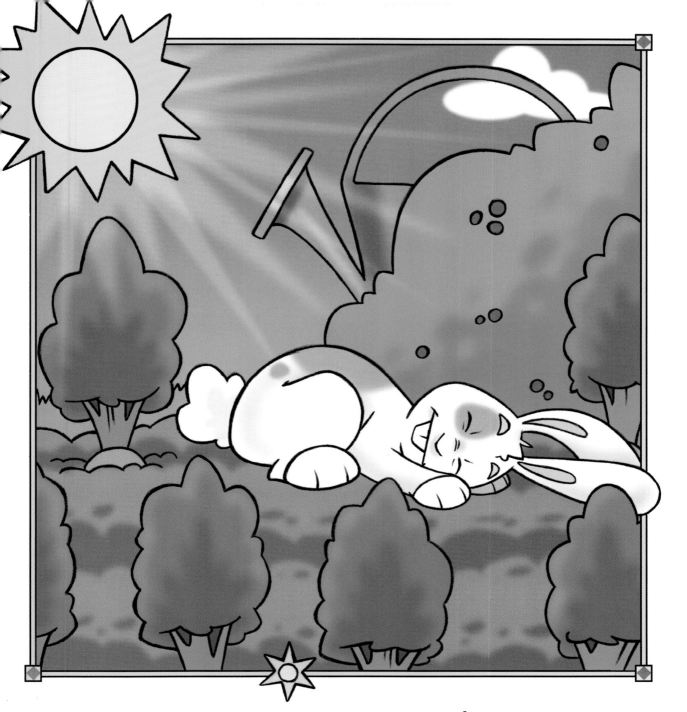

Hap can nap a bit.

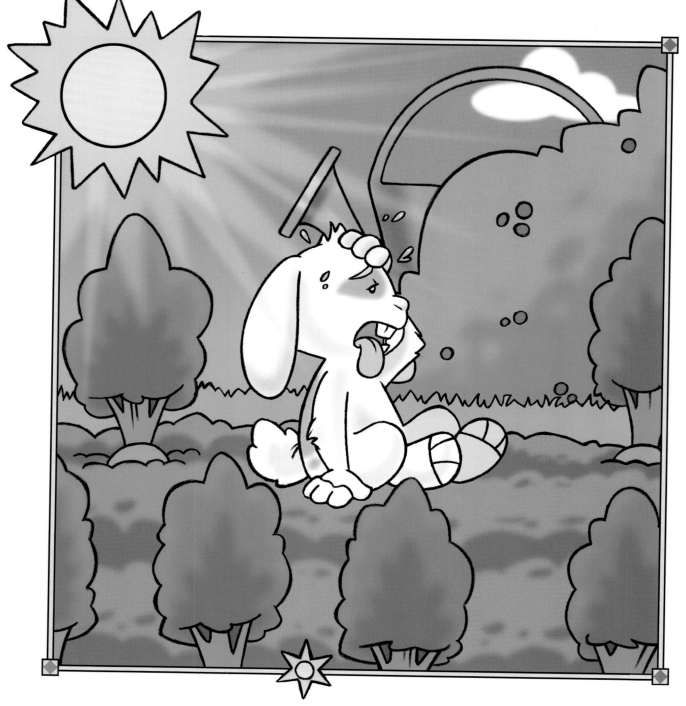

Hap, are you hot?

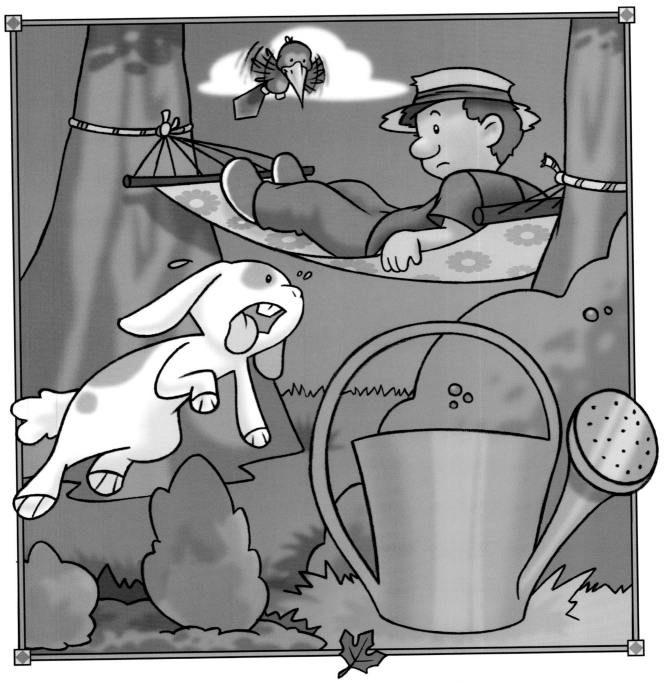

Hap, do not do that!

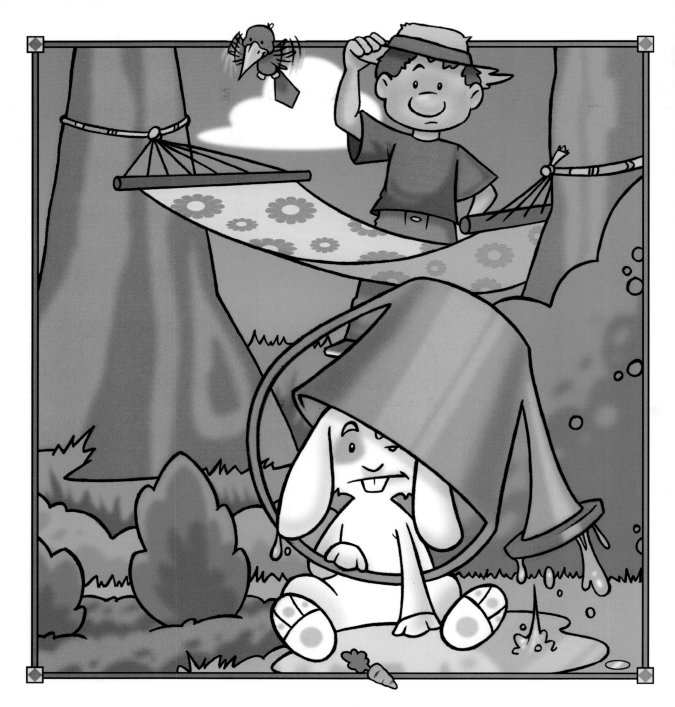

Hap did it.